Ravenscourt
B·O·O·K·S

The Labors of
HERCULES

By

Susan Blackaby

Illustrated by

David Groff

Columbus, OH • Chicago, IL • Redmond, WA

The McGraw-Hill Companies

SRAonline.com

 SRA

Cast of Characters

Apollo—god of prophecy

Athena—goddess of wisdom and war; daughter of Zeus

Atlas—god who holds the sky upon his shoulders

Geryon—giant who is part man and part beast

Hades—god of the Underworld

Hera—queen of the gods; wife of Zeus

Hercules—son of Zeus; hero of the story

King of Crete [Minos]—owner of the white bull

King of Elis [Augeus]—son of Poseidon; owner of stables

King of Mycenae [Eurystheus]—half brother of Hercules

King of Thrace [Diomedes]—son of Ares; owner of man-eating horses

Nemea—home of the terrible lion

Poseidon—god of the sea

Zeus—most powerful god; husband of Hera

— CHAPTER 1—

Hera's Plot

The story of Hercules comes from Ancient Greece. At that time and in that land, people believed in gods and goddesses who lived on the slopes of Mount Olympus. All the gods and goddesses had special powers. Each of them had a special talent. The gods and goddesses were immortal, which means they would never die. They were not, however, perfect. They had many faults, and because they were more powerful than humans, their faults were larger too.

Zeus was the most powerful god, and he ruled over all the gods and goddesses. He decided when the Sun would rise and set. He controlled the seasons and could send deadly storms down to the world of humans.

*Zeus was married to Hera. She was the queen of the Olympians and the goddess of marriage and women. Hera was the most powerful of all the goddesses, and she did not let the others forget it.

The endless days of peace on Mount Olympus became boring. For a little excitement, the gods and goddesses stirred up trouble with one another. When they tired of fighting among themselves, they made trouble for mortals. Mortals are humans; that is, they do not live forever. The poor mortals, however, never knew when the gods and goddesses would cause trouble.

The Ancient Greeks were great believers in fate. They believed that some things were beyond their control and in the hands of the gods. So the Greeks built temples to honor the gods and goddesses and made offerings to keep them happy. The humans would do anything to win favor with the gods* who ruled the heavens and controlled their fate.

But pleasing the gods could be quite a challenge. The gods were often moody and were determined to carry out their own plans. When this happened, even the temples and offerings made by the mortals would not stop the gods.

Of all the goddesses, Hera was the moodiest. Her beauty was matched only by her rotten temper. Everyone in the heavens, on Earth, and in the Underworld knew about Hera's mean streak. Crossing Hera could cause trouble for those on Mount Olympus. It could be deadly for mortals.

If there was one thing that made Hera angry, it was Zeus's feelings for humans. Zeus liked the people of Earth and often used his powers when people needed help. He treated people gently because he knew they were small and weak. Hera burned with jealousy when Zeus paid attention to his favorite humans—women. For those mortals, Hera's anger could last a lifetime.

No human felt the sting of Hera's anger more than Hercules, who was one of Zeus's sons by a mortal woman. Hera knew that Zeus favored Hercules over his other children, and this angered Hera. She was afraid Hercules would become too powerful, and Hera did not want that to happen.

Before Hercules was born, Hera started making plans. She wanted to make sure Zeus would not favor Hercules. Zeus had promised that his firstborn mortal offspring would become a king. So Hera made sure that another mortal son was born to Zeus before Hercules. That son would become the king of Mycenae.

Although Hera had kept Hercules from becoming king, that was not enough for her. While Hera was plotting against him, Hercules grew into a beautiful, strong baby. Everyone who saw him loved and admired him. Hera could not stand the attention everyone gave Hercules.

As Hercules grew, so did Hera's anger toward him. She would not rest until she came up with the perfect plan to get rid of Hercules once and for all. She knew she had to make his death look like an accident. If she didn't, Zeus would be very angry with her.

Hera sent two serpents into Hercules' room. The serpents were supposed to wrap themselves around the baby Hercules and strangle him in his sleep. But Hera overlooked one detail. She did not count on the baby's strength.

The next morning Hercules was found safe and sound in his crib, laughing with glee as he held a lifeless snake in each hand. It was plain to see that the baby had some of his father's special talents. Even Hera could not compete with Zeus's mighty power.

Hera watched Hercules grow up. Hercules became a large, strong man, skilled in archery, hunting, and wrestling. People admired Hercules, but they feared his special powers.

Hercules could be rough, and he often hurt his friends and teachers accidentally because he did not know how to control his own strength. However, Hercules always tried to use his strength to help those in need.

Once a king gave Hercules a reward for helping someone. The reward was marriage to the king's daughter. Hercules married the king's daughter, and the two of them were very happy together. They had three sons. Hercules had found peace.

Seeing Hercules content angered Hera. Hera did not want Hercules to be happy, so she planned to hurt Hercules and his family. Hera used her powers to confuse Hercules so he would not know what he was doing. Hera then tricked him into committing a terrible crime. When Hercules awoke from the spell, he found that he had thrown his wife and sons into a fire. They had burned to death.

Hercules was brokenhearted. He believed that his strength had gotten the better of him, as it had so many times in the past. He did not know that Hera had tricked him. Feeling terrible about what he had done, Hercules traveled far and wide looking for forgiveness. The gods were so angry that they would not forgive him. They did not know that Hera had put a spell on Hercules, and they could not understand how he could kill his family. Hercules promised to live a life of goodness, but even that was not enough to satisfy the gods.

At last Hercules went to a temple to see an oracle. An oracle was a person who carried messages from the gods to the mortals. Hercules threw himself upon the temple steps. "Please help me!" he cried. "How can I rid myself of this terrible pain?"

Apollo was the god of prophecy, or telling the future. Apollo would decide Hercules' fate. The oracle passed Apollo's message from Mount Olympus to Hercules.

Apollo's punishment for Hercules was harsh, but the rewards would be great.

"There is one thing you must do," the oracle told Hercules. "You must go to your half brother, the king of Mycenae, and you must do whatever he orders you to do. He will give you ten tasks to complete. Each one will be harder than the one before. You will be tested for many years. If you live, you will find peace, and you will become immortal like the gods."

Because of Hera's plotting, Hercules and his half brother, the cowardly king of Mycenae, were enemies even before they were born! For that reason, the king never missed a chance to do something to hurt Hercules. Even though Hercules did not like the idea of being ordered around by his half brother, he wanted to make up for his terrible crime. He agreed to do whatever his half brother told him to do. Hercules traveled to see the king at his palace.

The cowardly king greeted Hercules from his throne. He knew better than to stand face-to-face with Hercules. The king was a small man, while Hercules was large and tall. Hercules looked like a giant next to him.

Hercules sighed deeply. "I am at your service, Brother," he said. "You hold the key to my forgiveness and future happiness."

Seeing Hercules look so unhappy made the cowardly king feel very powerful. He decided that Hercules' first task would also be his last.

"So I have been told," said the king. "Shall we begin your punishment?" Hercules nodded.

"You need to do exactly what I tell you," the king continued. "You will be given ten labors, or tasks, to complete. Report to me after you finish each labor. Really, Hercules, it is so simple that even you can grasp it."

"I understand you and will try to do my best," said Hercules sadly. "What is my first labor?"

"It is a very small matter," said the cowardly king. "You must go to Nemea and kill the lion that lives there. Bring back its skin to show me that you have completed the first task."

Hercules could not believe that the king had asked him to kill the Nemean lion. "The Nemean lion is a monster," Hercules said. "Its father is a giant who causes Earth to rumble and who spits fire down the slopes of a mountain."

"Yes, that is the lion you must find and kill," said the cowardly king. "It is even bigger than you, Hercules. Now leave, and do not return without that hide."

Having been given the directions for the first labor, Hercules left the palace and began the trip to Nemea.

"Well, that is the end of Hercules," thought his half brother. "No one has ever battled the Nemean lion and lived. The lion is as big as an elephant, knives cannot cut its skin, and its claws can shred stone."

The king thought he never would see Hercules again, which made him very happy. The cowardly king had always been afraid Hercules would somehow become king in his place. After all, he was king only because Hera had tried to keep Hercules from the throne. At last the king felt free of his half brother, Hercules.

And so the labors of Hercules began.

CHAPTER 2

Bringing Down the Beasts

Hercules traveled into the mountains to kill the lion of Nemea. He took a strong net, a spear, and his favorite club. His club was very strong because it was made from a wild olive tree.

When Hercules reached the place where the lion lived, he heard the lion before he saw it. Its earsplitting roar shook the ground. When the great beast came charging toward him, Hercules first threw his spear at the lion. Hercules could throw a spear with enough force to split a tree trunk. But this time, the spear just bounced off the lion's chest as if the lion were solid rock.

Angered by the attack, the huge lion charged again. Staying far from the lion's claws, Hercules grabbed his club and swung it with all his might. Hercules hit the lion with a blow that would have killed anything else. But the lion was only stunned and turned away from Hercules. The huge beast headed for its den, and Hercules followed.

The lion's cave had two openings. Hercules used his net to block one of the openings so the lion could not escape. Then Hercules entered the cave at the other opening to surprise the lion.

The beast, no longer stunned, was angry. When the lion reared to attack, Hercules dodged its powerful claws. He tackled the lion and threw the huge beast to the ground. Hercules grabbed the lion's throat and choked the lion. Their fight shook the ground, but in only a few minutes the great beast lay dead at Hercules' feet.

To prove that he had killed the lion, Hercules had to take the lion's skin back to his half brother the king. Skinning the lion was not an easy job. It seemed that nothing would cut the lion's hide. In the end Hercules used the lion's claw to cut the skin. Hercules draped the hide over his back and wore the lion's head like a helmet.

When Hercules returned to the king's palace, he looked as if he were the Nemean lion. When the king saw Hercules bounding toward the city gates, he almost fainted. He thought Hercules was the lion! He thought the lion had killed Hercules and had come to the palace to kill him.

Soon the king realized that it was Hercules, not the lion. He was ashamed that he had been afraid, and so he grew angry with Hercules. "Hercules, you will not live to fool me again!" he shouted at his half brother from a distance. But Hercules was too far away to hear him.

*As he spoke those words, the king wondered how Hercules had killed the lion. The king knew that Hercules had amazing strength. He had seen Hercules prove his power many times. But he did not think Hercules could win a battle against a beast like the Nemean lion. Now he could see for himself that Hercules had the strength of a god in the body of a man.

That thought made the king freeze with fear, and he could not face his half brother. So the cowardly king of Mycenae sent his servant to stop Hercules from entering the city gates.

"Tell Hercules that he is not welcome in my city," the king said. "I forbid him to enter the gates ever again. From now on, you will tell him what he needs to do. Send him to the Hydra. Killing it will be his next labor."

Hercules was glad* to avoid his half brother. The servant told Hercules that his next labor was to kill the Hydra.

Hercules knew the Hydra was a monster that had special powers. The Hydra was a nine-headed serpent with fangs. When one of the heads was cut off, two grew back in its place. The Hydra could crush victims with its snakelike body or poison them with a bite. Even its breath could kill.

Before Hercules set out to kill the Hydra, he went to find his nephew, who was a chariot driver. Hercules thought that if he had to travel a long way for each of his labors, at least he could ride in a chariot.

Hercules carried a sword and a bow and arrows and wore the lion skin as protection. When Hercules and his nephew reached the swamp where the Hydra lived, Hercules shot arrows at the twisting monster hiding there. The arrows missed the Hydra coiled among the plants.

Hercules' arrows and club were useless against the Hydra. Holding his breath against the smell, Hercules tried to get his strong hands around one of the Hydra's many necks. No sooner did Hercules get a good grip on one head than another head would sink its fangs into him.

Hercules took up his sword and swung it again and again, chopping off the Hydra's heads. The heads doubled with every blow. Hercules cried for his nephew to help him.

"Light a torch!" Hercules shouted. "When I cut off one of the creature's heads, burn its neck. That will stop two new heads from springing from the stump!"

With his nephew's help, Hercules killed many heads of the Hydra. When only one head was left, Hercules struck a blow that sent the head flying. Then he buried the Hydra deep in the ground and put a huge rock on the grave to keep the Hydra in the ground.

Before leaving the swamp, Hercules stopped to dip his arrows in the Hydra's blood. There was a chance that the blood might have hidden powers, and Hercules hoped those powers would also help his arrows.

When Hercules returned, the king's servant met him at the city gates. The king himself was nowhere to be seen.

"The king wants me to tell you that killing the Hydra does not count as one of your labors because you got help from your nephew," said the servant. "You still must complete nine tasks."

Hercules was angry, but he was not allowed to argue his case. The king was hiding from Hercules in a large clay jar, and he would not come out of the jar until Hercules was gone.

The servant gave Hercules his third labor. "The king wants you to capture the golden-horned red deer. The deer belongs to the moon goddess. Do not harm the deer, for the king wants it alive."

Killing the red deer would not have been difficult. Hercules easily found its home, and his skill with a bow made the deer an easy target. But Hercules had to be careful. The moon goddess protected the deer. She would kill anyone who harmed or stole her golden-horned red deer.

Hercules spent months tracking the red deer through the forest. Whenever he got close enough to catch it, the deer would bound away.

After a year, Hercules grew tired of the chase. He hurt the deer with one swift shot of an arrow. He was carrying the deer on his shoulders when the moon goddess caught up with him. She was boiling with anger.

"How dare you!" she said. "You will regret harming an animal that I hold sacred. How would you like me to show you how it feels to be hunted? None of your weapons will stand up to my powers. Get ready to run for your life."

Hercules fell to his knees. "Dear goddess," he begged, "please do not punish me. I am already being punished more than any mortal can bear.

"My family is dead, and Apollo has sent me to do labors for my half brother. My only chance of forgiveness is to do what the cowardly king of Mycenae wants. If you want to blame someone for this terrible deed, please blame the king of Mycenae."

"The king?" said the goddess. "What does that cowardly little king have to do with this?"

"He demanded that I bring your golden-horned deer to his palace. I have no choice but to do whatever he says until I have completed my service to him." Tears streamed down Hercules' cheeks. He knew the moon goddess could kill him with just one look.

The goddess took pity on the strong hero. "Calm down, Hercules," she said. "I have heard of your troubles. I'll let you borrow my little red deer to complete your labor. If you put your hand on her golden horn, she will walk right by your side."

Hercules smiled with relief as the moon goddess continued. "See that you let her go when you reach the palace, and don't forget, you will feel my anger if you don't play by my rules," she said.

"Thank you," said Hercules. "I will take good care of her and send her back to you right away."

With that, Hercules left the goddess and led the little red deer to the city gates.

When the king heard that Hercules had returned with the red deer walking calmly beside him, the king was more frightened than ever. If Hercules could bring back the red deer, then he must have found favor with the moon goddess. The king quickly sent his servant to tell Hercules his next labor. The sooner Hercules was gone, the better.

On his way to the next labor, Hercules returned the red deer to the moon goddess. He knew it was wise to keep his word to a goddess.

CHAPTER 3

More Animals

Hercules' next labor was to capture a famous wild boar. A wild boar is like a pig with long, sharp tusks. This giant boar was known to have a nasty temper.

Hercules thought it would be easy to capture the wild boar. But things were never easy for Hercules. He had headed into the mountains where the wild boar lived when Hercules came across a group of centaurs. Centaurs are beings that are half man and half horse. The centaurs asked Hercules to join their party. The evening started out all right. Hercules was a friend of one of the centaurs, but the party soon turned into a battle. Hercules, fighting for his life against the centaurs, shot at them with his arrows that had been dipped in the Hydra's blood. A poisoned arrow struck Hercules' friend, who died in pain.

A sad Hercules continued up the mountain alone. It was winter, and he knew that the boar was holed up in its cave. Hercules hid in some bushes near the opening of the cave. Then he made a lot of noise.

The boar raced outside to see what was happening. Hercules let out an earsplitting roar and scared the boar so badly it began running through the mountains. When the boar grew too tired to run any farther, it fell into a snowdrift. Hercules quickly threw a net over the boar and captured it.

Hercules carried the boar back to the king to prove he had completed his labor. The king peeked out of his jar long enough to see the long, sharp tusks of the huge pig. After that, the king would have nothing to do with Hercules or with the boar. But he wanted to teach Hercules a lesson for making this labor seem so easy.

*"Send him to clean out the stables that belong to the king of Elis," said the king from deep inside his jar. "And tell him he has to do it in just one day."

The king of Elis lived in a land far away, where he raised cattle by the thousands. Hercules could smell the stables from miles away.

"Well, well," Hercules greeted the king of Elis, "you have quite an animal kingdom here, I must say. How long has it been since you cleaned out your stables?"

"Thirty years or more," he said. "I don't suppose you have come here to work as my stable boy." The king laughed. "I don't pay stable boys, you know."

"I see that you don't," said Hercules. "But I can make you a deal. I'll clean out your stables in one day, and you can pay me with some of your finest steers.* How does that sound?"

"It sounds too good to be true," the king said. "I'd like to see you do it."

The king of Elis sent his son to watch Hercules work. Hercules went down to the stables, shovel in hand. But he did not begin to shovel out the stalls. Instead, he cut two large holes in the wall around the cattle yard.

Hercules then made a dam by heaping mounds of dirt and stones. Hercules used the dam to change the course of two nearby rivers. Instead of flowing around the stables, the river water rushed into the cattle yard. The flood cleared the dirt out of the stables and carried it out the other side of the cattle yard. The rushing water left the stables fresh and clean.

"I'll just take my cattle now and be on my way," said Hercules.

But the king of Elis refused to give the cattle to Hercules. "Don't play games with me, Hercules," he said. "I know that the king of Mycenae ordered you to clean out my stables, whether it took one day or one year. I don't owe you anything, and I will not give you any of my cattle."

Hercules returned to his half brother's palace without a reward for cleaning out the stables. The king's servant met him at the city gates.

"The king wishes me to inform you that he will not count your last labor," the servant told him.

"What do you mean?" shouted Hercules. "He did not count the Hydra, and now he is not going to count this? Doesn't he know that I cleaned out the stables for the old king in just one day?"

"Yes, but the king says you cannot be paid for these labors, Hercules," explained the servant. "You must perform them for free. It is part of your service."

"I was not paid!" protested Hercules.

"You may not have been paid, but you were hired to do the job. The fact that the king of Elis did not pay you makes no difference," said the servant.

Hercules did not think his half brother the king was being fair, but he knew it was useless to argue. The king's servant told Hercules that his next labor was to rid the world of a deadly flock of man-eating birds. The birds lived near a lake hidden deep in the woods. No one had been able to destroy them. The birds belonged to the god of war. These man-eating birds struck fear into the heart of anyone who came near them.

Hercules tried to find a way to kill the birds, but he couldn't get a clear shot at them. They were roosting in the thick branches of the trees around the lake, and they stayed hidden.

Hercules failed over and over again to get near the birds because he kept sinking into the marsh. At last he asked the goddess Athena for help.

"I am pleading with you, Athena, goddess of wisdom, goddess of war," cried Hercules. "Only you can help me destroy these terrible birds."

Athena heard Hercules and took pity on him. She understood Hercules' hardships. Athena went to ask the god of fire to make a metal rattle. The rattle made an extremely loud noise. Athena gave it to Hercules.

"Take this rattle to the mountain overlooking the lake," said Athena. "When you shake it, the sound will echo through the woods and frighten the birds. Once you flush the birds, they cannot escape your arrows."

"Thank you, goddess," said Hercules. "I am grateful to you for your help."

Hercules took the rattle to the mountain as Athena had told him to do. When he shook it, it made an earsplitting noise. The birds flew out of hiding, and Hercules soon killed all of them.

Hercules was not supposed to get help with his labors. The king might not have counted this labor, but he knew better than to question Athena. He wisely gave Hercules credit for this task.

CHAPTER 4

Wits and Wars

Hercules was now halfway through his years of service. He was anxious to get on with the next labor.

The king's servant gave Hercules his orders. "You will travel to the island of Crete and bring back the white bull."

Hercules boarded a ship to Crete. As he sailed over the sea, he wondered how he would complete this task. The bull had been a gift to the king of Crete from Poseidon, god of the sea. The king of Crete had promised to sacrifice the bull to Poseidon, but when he saw how great the bull was, he kept it for himself. He hid the bull in his own herd and sacrificed a plain bull in its place.

When Poseidon learned that the king had tricked him, he drove the bull mad and set it loose to cause problems all over the island. Legend said the bull could not be tamed.

Hercules did not know how he would capture the bull. The bull did not hide in a cave like the other beasts Hercules had hunted. It tore over Crete, destroying crops and buildings and scaring people. It was not long before Hercules tracked down the bull.

Hercules grabbed the bull's horns and brought the huge, crazed beast to its knees. He then dragged it onto the ship and tied it up for the long voyage.

When the trip ended, the bull was calm.

The servant met Hercules as he was leading the bull to the city gates. "The king does not want to keep the bull," he said.

"Well, what shall I do with it?" asked Hercules. "I cannot take it back to Crete!"

"Let it run free," said the servant. "I'm sure it will not be a problem. It seems to be perfectly tame."

Hercules untied the rope and let the bull loose. Right away it began to snort and buck. When the bull was away from Hercules' control, its madness returned. The bull took off, kicking, leaping, and destroying everything in its path. It spent years causing trouble all over the land.

For Hercules' next labor, he was sent to the plains of Thrace.

"The king says you are to bring him the man-eating horses that belong to the king of Thrace," said the servant.

The king of Thrace was the son of the god of war. Not only did the king have a very bad temper, he was also a very rude host. It was his custom to serve his guests to his man-eating horses for dinner.

*For this labor, Hercules traveled with a small group of friends. When Hercules and his friends arrived, the king of Thrace invited them to dinner. Hercules knew this was a trick. He knew he would have to take care of the king before he could do anything about the horses.

"I would be honored, of course," said Hercules. "But I have been sitting around on a ship. I need to work up an appetite. I would challenge you to a wrestling match, but I would not want to hurt you."

"Hurt me?" the king said. "Don't make me laugh. I can beat you with one hand tied behind my back. You are a strong young man, but remember that my father is the god of war. I would be glad to wrestle with you. Then, after I win, dinner will be served."

And so Hercules and the king of Thrace* wrestled. The king proved to be a strong foe. Taking him down took a lot of effort.

The king of Thrace put up a good fight, but Hercules at last was able to pin him to win the match. Held fast in Hercules' grasp, the king was too tired to struggle. Hercules took advantage of his weary host and quickly served him to his own horses. They were very hungry and had tired of waiting for their evening meal.

As soon as the horses finished off the king, they turned into frisky, friendly beasts and posed no threat to Hercules and his friends. When the horses finished their meal, they lost their taste for human beings.

Hercules tied the horses to a chariot and drove them back to the palace. The king was scared to death of the man-eating horses, so he let them go.

"What is my next labor?" asked Hercules.

"The king wants you to get a small gift for his daughter," said the servant. "It is something she wants more than anything in the world."

"That does not sound so difficult," said Hercules. "What is it?"

"It is the belt of the Amazon queen. It was a gift from her father, the god of war," said the servant.

The Amazons were a warlike race of women. They were known for their skill with a bow. Hercules did not know what it would be like to confront the Amazon queen. He set sail for the land where the tribe lived. Again he took a small group of friends with him. When he arrived, he expected the worst and was ready to fight for the belt. However, he was happy to find the Amazon queen waiting to welcome him.

"Welcome to my kingdom, Hercules," she said. "What can I do for you?"

"Please come aboard so that we can talk," said Hercules. The Amazons on the dock watched the queen board Hercules' ship. They wanted to make sure she would be safe.

"I am sorry to be so bold," said Hercules. "I have to ask you for a favor. As you know, I am being tested. To succeed, I must take your belt to my half brother, the king of Mycenae. He wants to give it to his daughter."

"I understand your problem, Hercules," said the Amazon queen. "This belt has special meaning to me because it was a gift from my dear father. But I see that you need my help. I can give you what you seek. You need not worry about completing this labor. The belt is yours for the asking."

"Thank you," said Hercules. He was very happy and also very surprised. "You are both kind and generous. I will sing your praises to the heavens!"

Hercules smiled with relief. He was delighted. "This has been my most enjoyable— and my easiest—labor yet," he said.

When Hera found out that the Amazon queen was willing to hand over the belt, she flew into a rage. "That Amazon is such a silly fool," said Hera in disgust. "How dare she give in to Hercules this way! I cannot let him get away from the Amazons so easily. I will have to take matters into my own hands. The only way to stop him is to cause some trouble."

Hera turned herself into an Amazon servant girl so she could roam the dock. She walked among the Amazons, telling tales about Hercules. She said that Hercules and his friends were planning to carry out an evil plot to kidnap the queen. Hera's stories spread quickly through the crowd, and soon the Amazons rose to protect their queen.

The Amazons armed themselves and mounted their warhorses. They stormed the boat, taking Hercules and the Amazon queen by surprise.

When Hercules saw them coming, he jumped up and grabbed his bow.

"You are a liar!" he yelled at the Amazon queen. "You never meant to give me your father's belt. You meant only to hold me here so your army could come and kill me!"

"Believe me, Hercules," pleaded the queen, "that is not true! Here is the belt. Take it now! I have no wish to harm you or your men."

But Hercules did not believe the queen. He shouted for his friends to fight. In the battle that followed, Hercules killed the Amazon queen and snatched the belt from around her waist. He then helped his men fight off the rest of the Amazons so they could flee. At last the band got away and sailed for home.

CHAPTER 5

Double-Crossing

For the next labor, the king's servant told Hercules to go to an island in the West. "Bring the king the herd of cattle that belongs to Geryon," he ordered.

Geryon was a monster that was part man and part beast. He had the head, arms, and legs of three men growing out of one body. His prized cattle were watched by giants and a two-headed dog.

To reach the island, Hercules traveled far. He crossed mountain ranges and miles of desert to reach the sea. It was extremely hot. The heat caused Hercules great distress.

"I cannot stand this Sun beating on my back," he said. "The giant does not worry me, but I will not survive another moment of this heat."

*With that, Hercules fixed an arrow in his bow and sent it flying toward the Sun.

The Sun saw the arrow coming toward him. He was so impressed by Hercules' strength and aim that he gave Hercules a golden boat. Hercules used the boat to cross the sea.

When Hercules landed on the island, the two-headed dog picked up his scent and began tracking him. Hercules had just found the herd of cattle when the dog charged him, both heads barking and all its teeth showing.

Hercules lifted his club and stopped the dog with one blow. On the heels of the dog came one of the giants who tended the cattle for Geryon. When he saw what Hercules had done to his dog, the giant attacked. Hercules shot him with an arrow.

Word of the fight in the fields soon reached Geryon. When he learned that Hercules was* stealing the cattle, Geryon set out to kill Hercules.

Geryon came upon Hercules driving the cattle along the river to the place where his golden boat was tied up. The three-headed Geryon rose to stop Hercules, but Hercules was too quick for him. Hercules' arrows cut Geryon down.

Hercules loaded the cattle into the boat and sailed back across the sea. Once he returned to land, he gave back the boat and thanked the Sun. Then he started to drive the cattle east toward home.

Getting home with the herd was very hard. Hercules had to fight off robbers who wanted to steal the herd. He defeated them and kept going.

Then, as Hercules was driving the cattle along the shore, a bull broke free and ran into the water. It swam across the sea and went onshore where another of Poseidon's sons kept his own cattle.

Hercules left Geryon's cattle in the care of the god of fire. Then he was off to find the bull. He decided to go to Poseidon's son to get back the bull. Hercules demanded the bull be returned to him. But Poseidon's son refused.

"This bull wandered into my fields, so now it belongs to me," he said. "I am not going to give it to you just because you asked for it. We can wrestle for it. The man who wins the best of three matches can keep the bull."

Hercules agreed. He beat Poseidon's son fairly and took the bull back to the rest of Geryon's herd.

As Hercules was driving the cattle home, Hera stepped in to cause trouble again. Nothing she had put in Hercules' way had stopped him! This time she sent a swarm of flies to bite the cattle. The cattle went mad and ran into a river to avoid being bitten.

Hercules went after the cattle and rounded up as many as he could. He lost his temper when he reached the edge of the water for the second time. He blamed the water for scaring the cattle. He got even by filling the creek with rocks to stop its flow. Then he drove the cattle across the rocks and on to his half brother's palace.

As soon as the king received the cattle, he sacrificed them to Hera to stay in her favor. Then he told the servant to have Hercules bring back three golden apples from Hera's sacred tree.

"Where can I find this golden apple tree?" asked Hercules.

The servant shook his head. "No one knows. You will have to find it yourself."

To find the sacred tree, Hercules needed help from the gods. According to legend, the old man in the sea would know where to find the apple tree.

Hercules traveled far and wide to find the old man. At last the river spirits showed him where the old man slept. Hercules jumped onto the old man and held him down. The old man shifted into shape after shape, but Hercules did not let go.

"Leave me alone!" shouted the old man, twisting and tumbling. "Let go of me!"

"Not until you tell me where to find the tree," said Hercules, holding tight.

"Which tree ?" asked the old man.

"The tree that Hera and Zeus received as a wedding present from Earth. The tree that bears golden apples," said Hercules.

"You mean the tree guarded by the dragon?" said the old man.

"Yes, that must be the one," said Hercules. "Tell me where it is. I will not let you go until I know, so you might as well tell me."

"It is on the slopes of Mount Atlas," the old man said.

Hercules thanked the old man and the river spirits. The trip to Mount Atlas took him across many miles. Along the way he kept his ears open and got the advice he needed to complete his task.

On the mountain, Hercules found Atlas, the god who holds up the sky. Nearby was the sacred tree. It was filled with golden apples. Hercules saw a dragon twisting around the trunk of the apple tree. It flicked its tongue and hissed.

The dragon would not let Hercules get near the apples, but Hercules had been told that Atlas could pick as many apples as he wanted. Hercules needed help from Atlas, but Atlas had his hands full.

"Atlas, you must be tired of holding up the heavens year in and year out," said Hercules.

"I am," said Atlas, "but I have no other choice. I cannot let the heavens fall."

"Why don't you let me give you a break?" asked Hercules. "I'll hold up the sky for you, and you can rest your arms. While you are resting them, you can pick three golden apples for me. Does that sound fair to you?"

"It sounds fair," said Atlas. "Do you think you can handle the job, though?"

"I know I can do it," Hercules told him.

Atlas lifted the heavens onto Hercules' shoulders. Then he walked around the tree a few times, stretching his legs. The dragon blinked and went to sleep as Atlas walked up to it. Atlas plucked three apples from the tree. Then he returned to stand beside Hercules.

"You seem to be doing a fine job," said Atlas. He tossed an apple into the air and caught it. "I think you can take over my job."

"I don't think so," said Hercules. "This takes a tougher man than I am."

"You can do it," said Atlas. He started to walk away. "Wait!" shouted Hercules. He realized that he had been tricked, but he could not let the sky fall and go after Atlas. "Atlas! I'll take your job. I do not mind a bit. But, please, take back the sky long enough for me to get a pad for my shoulders. I am not as strong as you are."

Atlas came and took back the sky from Hercules. Instead of getting a pad, Hercules took the apples. "Thanks for the help," said Hercules. This time he walked away, leaving Atlas to his old job.

When Hercules returned to the palace, the king took the apples. He returned them to Hercules when he learned the apples could not be put down outside Hera's garden. The goddess Athena helped Hercules by returning the apples to the tree where they belonged.

CHAPTER 6

Fear and Freedom

For Hercules' last task, the king gave Hercules a labor he was almost certain to fail.

The servant met Hercules at the gate. "Where will my travels take me this time?" asked Hercules.

"The king wants you to go to the Underworld," said the servant.

In those days people believed that the spirits of everyone—good or bad—who died went to the Underworld and stayed there for all time. Those who had done evil deeds during their lives were punished there. Hades was the god of the Underworld.

"What do you mean? People from the land of the living cannot go to the Underworld without being trapped there," said Hercules.

*"Hades does not let people come and go as they please. What if I have to stay in the Underworld forever?"

"That is your problem. You are to go there and bring back the three-headed guard dog that belongs to Hades," said the servant to Hercules.

What if Hercules could never return to the land of the living? He did not want to risk the trip without being forgiven for some of the things he had done on Earth.

Over the years Hercules had many problems. His strength and his temper often worked against him. He had killed people he had not meant to harm. He had behaved badly time and again. He could not go into the Underworld without making sure that he would not be punished for his deeds on Earth. He did not want to suffer in the Underworld in the event that he had to* stay.

Hercules went to the temple and begged for help. It was said that the oracle there knew secrets that could protect Hercules against the spirits in the Underworld.

The oracle first cleared Hercules of all his mistakes and bad deeds. Then she helped make sure that Hercules would be happy in the Underworld in case he had to stay there. After that, Hercules was ready to go. He traveled to a dark cave leading inside Earth. He followed a path where there were many spirits and monsters. The messenger god and Athena stayed close by his side.

Deep inside Earth, Hercules found Hades, god of the Underworld, sitting on his throne.

"I am Hercules," he said. "I have come to ask you a favor that I know you have no reason to grant. I do not deserve your help, but I need it in order to fulfill my service in the land of the living."

"What is it you want?" asked Hades.

"I want to take your dog with me to the land of the living," said Hercules.

Hades thought about what Hercules asked. Finally he said, "Hercules, you can take my dog to the upper world with you, but only if you can lead him away using just your own strength. You cannot use any weapon against him."

Hercules agreed to the terms and went farther into the Underworld to find the monster dog. He expected a terrible creature. But when he came face-to-face with the dog, Hercules gasped. All three heads barked loudly. Its mouths slobbered, and its jaws snapped. Snakes across the dog's back reared up to strike. The serpent on the dog's tail hissed and spit.

Hercules did not waste any time. He threw himself at the beast. He grabbed the dog by its fur and knocked it to the ground. The snake on the dog's tail bit Hercules over and over. But its sharp teeth could not tear through the lion's hide that Hercules still wore.

The dog and the man wrestled, but Hercules slowly gained the upper hand. Hercules pinned the dog so that he could not fight back. Hercules forced the dog to give in.

Hercules carried the awful creature out of the Underworld and back through the cave to the land of the living. When he got to the king's palace, he insisted on seeing his half brother.

The king was shocked to hear that Hercules had returned. He peeked out of the jar where he was hiding, and he screamed when he saw the terrible dog growling and panting at Hercules' side.

"What do you want?" asked the king fearfully.

"I want you to meet the dog you asked me to bring to you," said Hercules. "And I want you to grant me my freedom. I have served you all these long years. I have completed the labors I was charged to do."

"Get that monster away from me!" cried the king.

"Shall I set it free to roam about your kingdom?" asked Hercules.

"No, no!" said the king. "I don't want it here! Take it back to Hades where it belongs! Take it back, and I will release you from service. You will have your freedom. Just get rid of that terrible dog! Go away now!"

"All right," said Hercules. "I will make sure that the dog is safely returned to the Underworld. You won't see the dog or me ever again."

"Just go!" said the king, sinking into his jar.

Hercules was finished at last. Upon completing the labors, Hercules was granted immortality, just like the gods.

Over time Hera stopped being angry with Hercules. She knew she had to learn to live with Hercules now that he had been granted immortality. Even so, Hera sometimes caused trouble for him just to remind him that she was more powerful.

Hercules had many more adventures. He often needed help from gods and goddesses. They smiled down on him in spite of all his faults.

Hercules' human life ended when he used one of the arrows dipped in the Hydra's blood to stop a centaur from attacking his new wife. The centaur cast a deadly spell on Hercules that ended his life.

When Hercules was at last lifted to Mount Olympus to take his place among the gods and goddesses, even Hera welcomed the hero home.

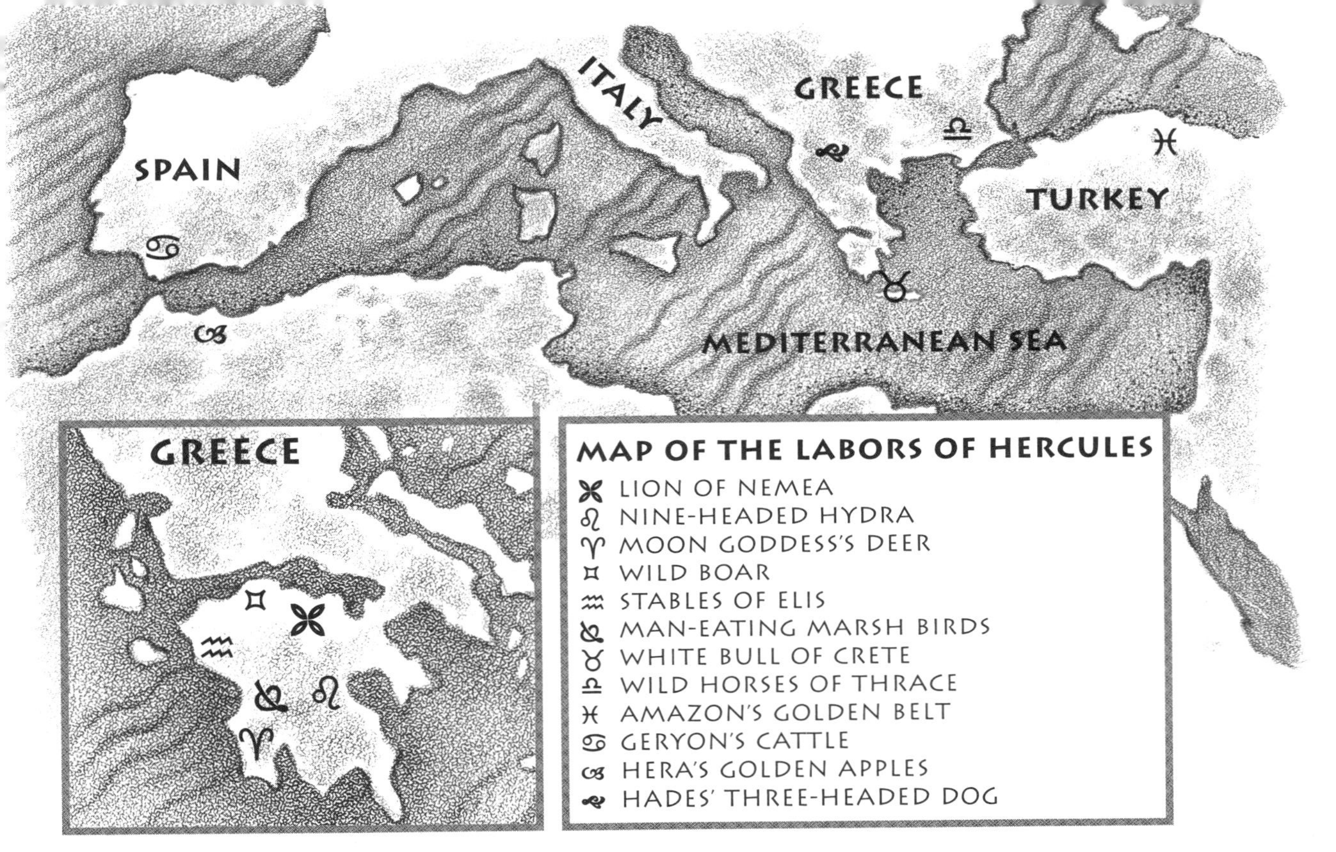
SPAIN
ITALY
GREECE
TURKEY
MEDITERRANEAN SEA
GREECE
MAP OF THE LABORS OF HERCULES
LION OF NEMEA
NINE-HEADED HYDRA
MOON GODDESS'S DEER
WILD BOAR
STABLES OF ELIS
MAN-EATING MARSH BIRDS
WHITE BULL OF CRETE
WILD HORSES OF THRACE
AMAZON'S GOLDEN BELT
GERYON'S CATTLE
HERA'S GOLDEN APPLES
HADES' THREE-HEADED DOG